Black
Children in Care:
Health
Hair & Skin

By Denise Lewis and Flora Awolaja

Acknowledgements

The publishers have made efforts to establish the ownership of all images reproduced in this publication.
None of the children portrayed in this publication are Looked After Children

Original idea and product concept by Denise Lewis
Text by Denise Lewis and Flora Awolaja
Creative design, typography and layout by Flora Awolaja
Edited by Professor Toyin Okitikpi
Email: positiveimageproject@hotmail.com

British Library cataloguing in publication data.
A catalogue record for this book is available from the British Library.

ISBN 978-0-9576471-0-7

© positiveimageproject Ltd 2014
Printed and bound in the UK by Contract Publishing UK, Cambridgeshire

Contents

Prologue

When I was a foster child my foster parents knew so little about black skin they took me to the doctor. They asked if my grey knees were the symptom of illness. They didn't know about cocoa butter.

My foster mother combed my hair with a thin-toothed comb used for Caucasian hair and, being a nurse, she would often use the hospital nit comb. It tore at my hair and stretched my scalp until my head felt scorched with hot water. Each morning I screamed. Take it from me; this book is a gift to save you time and stress and to allow you and your foster child to love the skin you're in. Yes, that's you too. This is about love, care and attention.

Treat this as an introduction into another world, and go out there with questions. Go to black hairdressers, and watch and ask, go to shops and stores. I was soooo nervous when I did it - I didn't know, really know, a black person until I was sixteen, seventeen - but I was so rewarded.

I only wish that my foster parents and the children's homes had had a book like this. As you enter the wonderful world of black hair and skin care, think how you are learning. How great learning is. How it lasts a lifetime. How great the human race is. How different and how similar we are.

I am thankful for my hair and I am thankful for my skin and my eyes and my blackness. We must be proud of who we are to cherish others. In this world we live in today self-image is important. It is armour and wings. What a gift to give to your foster child - armour and wings to travel, to grow and to be strong and open. What a wonderful book this is. Enjoy. Enjoy. **Lemn Sissay**

Foreword

It is estimated that there are over 60,000 children being looked after in the care system at any one time in the UK. In fact it is widely acknowledged that black children and children of mixed heritage constitute quite a high percentage of the total number of children in care. Why this is the case is not the subject of this book, but what is of interest is that children come into care for a variety of reasons, for example: wilful neglect, being beyond parental control, because of concerns about their welfare and/or lack of education, or they are subject to or at risk of significant harm and/or abuse (sexual, physical, psychological, and emotional).

Moreover, despite the difficulties children may have experienced and the unsuitability of their familial environment, they must get used to new surroundings and unfamiliar routines once they are taken into care. While their safety is of crucial importance, it is also essential to take care of their physical, emotional and psychological well-being; the importance of hair care, skin care, and health cannot be underestimated. In fact, it would not be an exaggeration to suggest that feeling safe and healthy, self-esteem and confidence are all inextricably linked to each other.

The documents **Every Child Matters** and **Safeguard Children** make explicit and implicit reference to the requirement that the needs of children should be at the forefront of all considerations. Black children and children of mixed heritage have additional requirements with regards to their health, hair care and skin care.

*2004 Department of Education: Foreword by Professor Toyin Okitiki

Who is this guide for?

This guide is aimed primarily at the parents, carers and legal guardians of black and mixed heritage children. Social workers, carers in residential settings and other people working with or bringing up black or mixed heritage children may also find the information useful.

The guide will also be useful for anyone with an interest in the health and well-being of black and mixed heritage children.

Looking after black children's hair, skin and health is not only about providing practical help; it is also about nurturing that crucial bond between parent/carer and child. Helping children to develop self-confidence and taking pride in their appearance is one of those parental roles that is not always acknowledged.

A child who feels loved and looked after is much more likely to develop a positive sense of self and a strong racial and cultural identity.

Introduction

Parents, carers and practitioners are often wary of publications that assume they have little or no understanding of the background or cultural needs of the children in their care or for whom they have responsibility. The need to take account of children's ethnicity, culture and religion is entrenched in all child care legislation. In fact, carers and practitioners with any involvement in looking after children have a duty to ensure that all aspects of the child's needs are taken into account and that every effort is made to address them. While carers and practitioners try to take account of children's background, their hair and skin care and health are not often at the forefront of their work.

One of the five key pillars of the Every Child Matters policy initiative is about children being supported to 'be healthy'. In our view, being healthy involves many dimensions and includes practical, psychological, emotional and physical aspects. How a child feels about him/herself and how he/she looks, could, we suggest, have a major impact on his/her sense of well-being and feeling of belonging.

Generally, there is a great deal of emphasis placed on the cultural needs of children from black and mixed heritage backgrounds, and efforts are made to address their self esteem.

However, it is our consideration that little or far less, consideration is given to their health, hair care and skin care. Anecdotal evidence suggests that while many carers and practitoners try to do their best, they appear to have little knowledge or Understanding of how to look after black children's hair and skin.

For example: one of the authors of this publication noted an instance where an African Caribbean girl was placed with white foster carers on a Friday evening and when the child was visited on the Monday morning her hair had been cut off.

The carers explained that they had tried to wash the child's hair but it became tangled and they felt their only option was to cut it. In another case, a white foster carer asked if it would be alright to use cooking oil to moisturise an African Caribbean child's skin. These might be isolated cases, but it is also possible that such lack of knowledge about how to care for black and mixed heritage children is wide spread.

Children going into care and being looked after often lose contact with members of their extended family and then don't hear stories about their childhood or stories about their racial

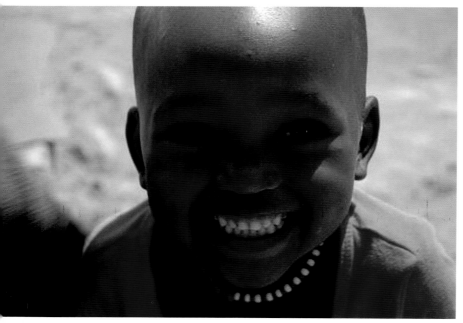

and cultural background. Just as importantly, they also miss out on the learning experience of watching how others in the family care for their hair and skin.

This guide aims to fill that gap by providing the information needed to facilitate better knowledge and understanding. Therefore empowering foster carers, adoptive parents, and other professionals looking after black children and mixed heritage children in the care system who are in cross-cultural placements.

Hair care

Facts about hair

Hair is made up of 90% keratin, a tough protein that also makes up skin and nails.

Hair consists of three main layers:

Medulla: the centre of the hair shaft.

Cortex: gives the hair strength.

Cuticle: acts as a protective layer, covering the hair shaft.

Washing the hair

As every child's hair is different, carers need to consider how best to manage their child's hair. It is important to be aware that African Caribbean hair shrinks when wet. Black children's hair does not need to be washed daily, as that will remove the natural oils in the hair, making it dry. When washing your child's hair, rinse with warm water, and gently comb your fingers through the hair. Use a shampoo specifically for black hair *[see online resources under 'Natural hair care']*. Put some shampoo on your hands, and then work the shampoo through the hair, parting the hair in sections as you go along. Massage the hair gently, for approximately 5-10 minutes, rinsing with warm water. Apply conditioner and repeat the process, then rinse thoroughly and dry gently with a towel.

Combing the hair after washing

Comb wet hair using a wide tooth comb with round-edged teeth. Comb hair gently, parting sections of the hair one at a time. Add hair moisturiser to the scalp, distributing it evenly through the hair. Moisturiser is essential after washing to maintain a healthy sheen, as well as locking in moisturising oils that will prevent the hair from drying and breaking. Comb the moisturiser through, finally plaiting the hair in a **protective style *[see Glossary]***.

Combing products

Keeping a good hair regime requires not only quality products appropriate for black hair, but also the proper tools for styling. Curly hair require quality brushes and combs both to bring out the best in the hair and also to avoid unnecessary damage and breakage. Always use a **wide-tooth comb** *[see Glossary]* (the wider the better), pick, or curl detangler when combing the hair. Curly hair is extremely fragile. A gentle touch is required to avoid unnecessary breakage and hair loss. Avoid fine tooth combs as they snag and pull out the hair.

Grooming products

Shea butter: For centuries, Shea butter has been used as a natural hair stimulant. Shea butter is extracted from nuts that grow on the shea-karite tree (*Vitellaria paradoxa*), found only in the tropics of Africa. The nut has a high content of fatty acids. As it is full of minerals, vitamins, moisturising and anti-inflammatory properties, shea butter has many benefits for the hair. Its anti-inflammatory properties heal a damaged scalp and help clear any infection. It works well against dandruff too. Damaged hair can be conditioned and revitalised by its moisturising properties. As shea butter is light and non-greasy, it can also be applied as a leave-in conditioner. Using shea butter will help to stimulate hair growth because of its rejuvenating minerals and vitamins.

It's best to buy raw unrefined shea butter, as it retains the beneficial properties of antioxidants, essential fatty acids and minerals. Regular use of hair care products that provide moisture to the hair is one way to nourish and aid the hair to grow and stay healthy.

Coconut oil a plant-based oil is extracted from the kernel of the coconut with a high concentration of saturated fatty acids, lauric acid, capric acid and vitamins E and K. In its natural unprocessed state, coconut oil penetrates the hair shaft. Because it has a high moisture-retaining capacity it does not break down or evaporate easily when it is applied to the hair.

Applying coconut oil to the hair shaft and ends leaves the hair soft and shining. It can be massaged into the scalp to stimulate the roots and hair follicles, which promotes hair growth. Coconut oil is a natural oil for black hair because it is a highly effective moisturiser; it helps to lock in moisture deep at the hair shaft. Coconut oil's high concentration of fatty acids nourishes the hair with protein, making it healthy, strong and resilient.

Other natural oil: Using natural oils such as jojoba or avocado in children's hair is a good way to add strength, promote growth, retain hair length and moisturise dry hair. Natural oils are good because of the essential fatty acids and minerals they contain. These are useful for achieving and maintaining healthy hair.

Plaiting the hair

Section the hair, by first parting it in the middle, from the crown of the head to the back of the neck. Then part the hair from ear to ear across the top of the head, to form a cross-type pattern on the top. Taking each quarter section, and three strands of hair, take the right hand strand and overlap with the middle strand. Then take the left strand and overlap to the middle. Repeat the process until the plait begins to form.

Hair textures and care tips

Black hair is unique in its structure and appearance and needs to be treated very carefully. It is at its weakest when wet, and can break easily. Black hair can be classified into three basic types:

Wavy: Soft or deep waves and little to no curl. Coarse and stays close to the scalp in long 's' shaped curves.

Care tips for wavy hair

Invest in a good -'bristle brush'- to keep the waves smooth. Use a light moisturising hair gel to add definition to the waves. Deep condition regularly and use a moisturising leave-in conditioner.

Curly: Fine and soft. It doesn't have a lot of sheen. It has lots of body. Curly hair straightens when it is wet and curls as it dries.

Care tips for curly hair
Only use wide tooth combs, the wider the better. Use deep conditioner after shampoo. Use moisturiser daily. To reduce frizz, do not brush the hair. Do not use towels to dry curly hair. Use a hair dryer to dry, or blow dry on medium with a diffuser attachment instead.

Kinky: The most highly textured of all the black hair types is very tightly curled – wirey. It is also the driest and most fragile of all the hair types, especially when wet.

Care tips for kinky hair

Comb and detangle the hair when wet and coat with conditioner. Always use a wide tooth comb, fingers or a hair pick to detangle. Condition the hair with protein, oil, and moisture daily to keep it healthy and strong. After washing, use a moisturising leave-in conditioner.

African Caribbean hairstyles

Cornrow and Afro style   Cornrow   Cornrow with beads

African Caribbean hairstyles

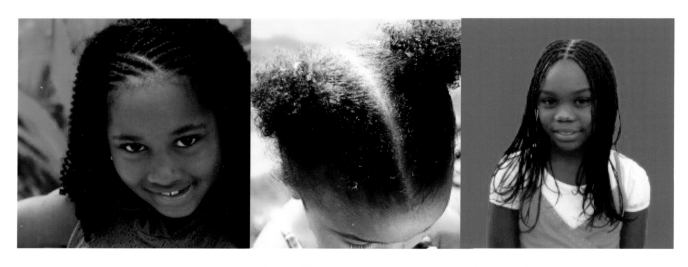

Cornrow with curly
hair extensions

Afro puffs

Plaits with hair extensions

A history of cornrow hairstyles

Cornrow is a hairstyle in which the hair is picked up and gathered along a row to form a tight plait against the scalp. Historical evidence from hieroglyphs and sculptures in Africa dating back thousands of years shows how much attention Africans paid to their hair. The clay sculpture (opposite) with cornrows is from the ancient Nok civilisation of Nigeria and may date back as far as 500 BC. Plaits have even been found etched at the back of the head of the sphinx. Like African art and architecture, cornrow styles shows the use of intricate, stylised geometric designs, as seen in this photograph of a Mende woman from Sierra Leone.

Mende woman; Sierra Leone

© Mende style by Rebecca Busselle 1970

Cornrows can be styled in a variety of different patterns. They are often used to add decoration or adornment to the hair. It is not uncommon to add beads into the plaits.

Cornrow hairstyles in Africa have come to represent different aspects of life, be it religion, kinship, status, age or ethnicity. Other attributes of identity can also be expressed in hairstyles.

Plaiting hair has cultural and communicative significance, particularly between a mother and her daughter. It is a skill that is passed down through the generations. Plaiting hair is also a time that can be used to develop a strong bond with children.

How to cornrow: A step-by-step guide

Part the hair for individual cornrow.

Divide the hair section into 3 parts.

Begin to plait small section of hair at the hairline.

Continue to plait hair, adding hair from the section you are plaiting into the cornrow.

Detangle hair when working your way through sections.

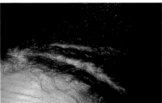

Individual cornrows begin to take shape. Continue to repeat process all the way around until completion.

Continue to plait hair, adding more hair into the cornrow.

Caring for locs

Maintaining a good hair regime will ensure healthy locs. Adding a moisturiser aids hydration prevents breakage and itching. Locs need protecting from breaking, lint and the elements. Putting locs into protective styles *[see Glossary]* at night and covering with scarves also protects them. Locs can also be protected by taking individual sections and braiding or twisting them. If the locs are difficult to handle, either pull them up or cover them.

Keeping locs clean

Locs do not need to be washed every day. Trial and error will usually determine what works best but once every two weeks should suffice. But it is important to check regularly for lint and other particles.

Caring for your Afro

Hair and grooming have always played an important role in the culture of Africa. Afro hair is a term used to refer to the natural texture of hair of Black African hair that has not been altered by Hot Combs, Flat Irons, or chemicals. The Afro as a hair style first emerged in the 1950s and was worn by artists, dancers and musicians including Odetta, Mariam Makeba, and Nina Simone.

In the 1960's the style became popular during the Black Civil Rights, and Black Power Movements. The Afro hair style is created by combing out the hair away from the scalp, allowing the hair to extend out from the head in a large rounded shape.

Caring for the Afro

Maintaining an Afro involves everyday attention and special care. You should shampoo your hair no more than once a week, after which you use

an instant conditioner to make the hair soft and manageable. Use a deep conditioner at least once a month, and after washing your hair allow it to dry naturally, by gently using a towel, rather than use a hair dryer. To keep the Afro hair in good condition moisturise the hair, plait and oil the hair with Coconut oil, or shea butter. At night when sleeping tie the hair in a scarf, to keep it tidy.

Taking care of an Afro requires gentle handling to keep tangles to a minimum, and to maintain well-moisturised hair, using the right styling comb is a must, so using 'picks' and wide-toothed combs are necessary. Eating well is essential to maintain healthy hair, whether you eat small meals throughout the day, or three big meals ensure that you include a balance of fruits, lean meats and vegetables, in your diet.

skin care

Skin care

Black and mixed heritage children must moisturise their skin daily to prevent their skin becoming dry. If this occurs, carers need to apply more moisturiser. Shea butter and cocoa butter are recommended. Eating a balanced diet and drinking water are also beneficial for healthy, glowing skin. Chlorine in public swimming pools is extremely damaging to both their skin and hair. Children of all ages should wear swimming caps in the water and shower immediately afterwards with soap to remove the chlorine. Moisturiser should be applied immediately after swimming. The perception that black children do not have to worry about skin cancer is false. Black and mixed heritage children can get skin cancer and should wear sunscreen and a hat when playing outside to prevent sunburn.

Organic skin products

Organic skin products contain natural ingredients such as yogurt, cucumber, lavender, chamomile, avocado, tea tree oil, honey and olive oil. These products are better for the skin and usually do not cause the irritation that some non-organic products can cause. A large number of skincare products include alcohol. This can be extremely dry for sensitive skin conditions like eczema. Some ingredients in organic skin care products occur naturally and are more easily absorbed by the body.

Tea tree oil: Melaleuca leucadendron

Natural skin care

Why use natural skincare products? Around 60% of skincare products are absorbed into the bloodstream when you put them on your skin. Therefore, it is important to know what ingredients are in the products you use. Natural skin care is the care of the skin using natural ingredients such as jojoba, shea butter, witch hazel, aloe vera, tea tree oil and chamomile, combined with **natural soap** or **oils.** Many people use natural skincare recipes to make their own products to care for their skin. These natural products can be made specifically to the individual's skin type or skin condition. Your skin is amazing: help it stay that way.

TIPS TO MAINTAIN GOOD SKIN CONDITION

1. Opt for natural ingredients, e.g. plant-based oils and butters such as coconut oil, olive oil, shea butter and cocoa butter.
2. Research skincare ingredients that should be avoided, e.g. parabens, lauryl sulphates and phthalates are reported to have harmful effects on the body.
3. Read the label of skincare products carefully, even the ones that say 'natural'. If in doubt, leave alone!
4. Eat fresh fruit and vegetables that are rich in vitamins and minerals.
5. Drink plenty of water to keep you hydrated.
6. Exercise regularly to help the flow of oxygen to the skin.
7. Get a good night's sleep, as this helps to repair your skin while you sleep.

Moisturising creams

Carers should look for unscented and alcohol-free moisturisers that suit their child's skin type in order to avoid irritation. Moisturising creams such as cocoa and shea butter are ideal. It is important to apply to the lips and face.

Moisturisers that are appropriate for the body may not be suitable for the more delicate skin of the face.

Eczema

Eczema, also known as dermatitis, is a non-contagious skin condition. It is an itchy inflammation of the skin and is common among African Caribbean children. Eczema can be difficult and embarrassing for anyone, but for African Caribbean and mixed heritage children with eczema there are many more concerns, including disfiguring and discolouring of the skin *[hyperpigmentation – see Glossary].* Eczema is generally more common in children than in adults.

The most common type of eczema is **atopic eczema [see Glossary]**. This occurs when the immune system overreacts to ordinary substances. It is accompanied by severe scratching and itching. The common treatment for atopic eczema is to apply topical creams and steroids that help to hydrate the skin. In contrast to white skins, the condition in black and mixed heritage children looks different. It may look dry, ashen or have grey patches, making

diagnosis difficult. Avoiding stress and allergic triggers, e.g. cheese, dairy products; a healthy diet and using approved medicated creams can offer some relief. All children with eczema need to modify bathing habits, skin care products and other chemicals that come into contact with the skin.

Natural remedies for eczema

There are many medical remedies to treat the symptoms of eczema, but many people prefer to take a natural and holistic approach. Using natural remedies helps to treat eczema with fewer side-effects and less harm to the skin. Certain nutrients, e.g. omega-3 oil, and some herbs and essential oils can bring some relief to the symptoms of eczema, such as itching [see table opposite].

Calendula

Herb/Natural Remedies	Peppermint	Tea tree oil	Oatmeal	Patchouli
Treatment	Effective at relieving itching.	Good at clearing up eczema patches. It works to relieve itching, redness and swelling. It is a great anti-inflammatory, antiseptic and astringent.	Very good at relieving itching, softening the skin and reduce the redness. Taking a bath with oatmeal can be very soothing to the skin and helps to exfoliate and unclog skin pores.	Generally works as an antiseptic, and effectively controls eczema, when applied topically.
Solution	Rubbing a drop of diluted peppermint oil over the affected area usually gives some relief.	Tea tree oil can be applied topically to the skin to treat acne, burns and infections. It can also be used as a cleanser, lotion or cream.	For best results, tie a handful of natural oatmeal in a cheesecloth or fine muslin, and keep circulating in warm bath water. Afterwards apply aloe vera gel for relief.	

Dietary Supplements	Omega 3 Oils	Flaxseed Oil	Marine Phytoplankton	Pumpkin Seeds
	Essential fatty acids [EFAs] can be found in most oily fish, e.g. sardines, herring or mackerel.	Including a wide range of EFAs in the diet can be beneficial to the skin. EFAs are found in walnut oil, and linseed oil.	This supplement can be found at most health stores and is high in vitamins and minerals that help new cell growth and function.	Pumpkin and sunflower seeds are rich in zinc, and are a good source of anti-inflammatory fats.

Aromatherapy: Ayanna aromas

'Making life Fragrant' Medical Herbalist, Aromatherapist BSc (Hons), ITEC, ITHMA, MIPTI

Ayanna uses naturally sourced products, organic where possible, to convey health and well-being. With lots of experience in treating children's skin conditions, she has created **'Keziah Skin Cream'** for eczema and **'Skin Heal'** cream for psoriasis. Her **'Anushka's cradle cap oil'** does much more than the name suggests. A healer of conditions affecting the scalp such as dermatitis, and psoriasis, these products are excellent for use in parents and children. A qualified medical herbalist and Aromatherapist, Ayanna offers workshop facilities and private consultations, with three products for everyday use: **Shea Shampoo, Shea Delight, Shea Surprise**. Ayanna also creates specific herbal-based oils for children with challenging behaviour.

Health

Sickle cell anaemia

Sickle cell is an inherited red blood cell disorder. The most serious and common sickle cell disorder is sickle cell anaemia. Sickle cell trait is a milder form. Most people affected by sickle cell anaemia are either of African or Caribbean origin. Sickle cell affects the red blood cells, which become hard and sticky, and take on a sickle, or crescent, shape. When the sickle-shaped cells travel through small blood vessels, they clog the vessels and can block blood flow. In addition, the sickle cells die earlier than normal blood cells, leading to a constant shortage of red blood cells.

Recognising a sickle cell crisis

Pain associated with sickle cell disease can be disabling. When a sickle cell crisis occurs, bones and joints can become very painful, making activities like climbing stairs or walking difficult. Carers need to keep an eye out for a possible sickle cell crisis, characterised by one of four symptoms:

Bone crisis: An acute or sudden pain in a bone, usually in an arm or leg, which may become tender.

Acute chest syndrome: Shortness of breath. Severe pain can accompany acute chest syndrome in a young person with sickle cell anaemia.

Abdominal crisis: Pain in an abdominal crisis is sudden and constant, and may or may not be localised to any one area of the abdomen. Nausea, vomiting and diarrhoea may or may not occur.

Joint crisis: Acute and painful joint crisis can develop without a significant traumatic history. Pain occurs in single or multiple joints, restricting mobility because of the pain.

How to deal with a sickle cell crisis

One way carers can help their child deal with the effects of sickle cell is to reassure and empower them. It is important that children with sickle cell understand and know about their condition. Carers can encourage children to remain healthy, avoid infection, and drink plenty of fluids. Carers can also record the triggers that cause a sickle cell crisis, for instance exposure to cold. Dealing with sickle cell involves understanding the condition and keeping up-to-date medical records. Considering the likelihood that a sickle cell crisis will occur again, carers should arrange regular check-ups for the child with their GP or haematologist.

© Felix Mizioznikov/Shutter stock

Exercise

Being fit, healthy and active has social, emotional and intellectual benefits for the child. Improved emotional well-being helps children feel more comfortable, happy and relaxed, and raises their self-esteem. Parents can set a good example by being active themselves. Exercising together can be fun for everyone, and competitive sports can help children stay fit.

Regular exercise helps children feel less stressed.
Feel better about themselves.
Feel more ready to learn in schools.
Keep a healthy weight.
Build and keep healthy bones, muscles, and joints
Sleep better at night.

WHY EXERCISE

Children who exercise:
- **Feel better about themselves**
- **Are more physically fit**
- **Have more energy**

Other benefits of exercise are:
- **A lower risk of heart disease and diabetes**
- **Healthy bones and muscle growth**
- **Staying at a healthy weight**

Children should have many chances to run, cycle and play sports during the day. It is recommended that children get at least 60 minutes of moderate exercise daily. Moderate activity means you breathe harder, and your heart beats faster than normal. Examples of this are: walking fast, playing chase or tag, swimming, and playing an organised sport such as football, netball or basketball.

Younger children have a shorter attention span than older children; they may be active for 10-15 minutes at a time. The goal, however, is still to aim for a total of 60 minutes of activity every day.

Nutrition

Nutrition and diet

Good nutrition begins at home. The condition of your child's health, hair and skin can be attributed to what they eat. The food choices made by adults for children during the crucial years of their development can mitigate future health risks and lay the foundation for good food habits in later life.

Eating a healthy balanced diet

A structured eating plan with regular meals is important to establish good eating habits. Children need a nutrient-packed diet that provides all the essential building blocks for healthy growth of hair and for their general development. Meals and snacks should be made up of some of the five main food groups. [see table overleaf]. Water is best drunk between meals. Sharing healthy meals together, as a family, instils a positive attitude to food and helps to bond parents/carers and children.

THE FIVE MAIN FOOD GROUPS

Milk/Dairy products

These should be eaten in moderation because of their high saturated fat content, but they are an important source of calcium, which is essential for healthy bones and teeth. Good sources of calcium; milk, cheese, yoghurt, fromage frais, fortified orange juice, green vegetables and cereals.

Proteins

From hair to fingernails, protein is a major functional and structural component of all cells. Protein provides the body with roughly 10 to 15% of its dietary energy, and is needed for growth and repair. Proteins can be found in meat, poultry, fish, shellfish, eggs, pulses, nuts and soya.

Fats/Sugars

These foods, although an important energy source, often contain few other nutrients. This group includes foods such as cakes, biscuits, sweets, sugar-sweetened drinks and crisps. It is important not to have too many foods from this group too often.

Fruit and Vegetables

These are a great source of nutrients and are vital for a healthy diet. They can be eaten as part of every meal, as well as being the first choice for a snack. Children should try to eat at least five portions of fruit and vegetables each day.

Starchy Foods

This food group contains the starchy carbohydrates that are the body's main source of energy. It includes, bread, pasta, rice, noodles, chapatti, cereals and other carbohydrates. This food group should make up a third of the diet.

Healthy Caribbean food

Children moving to a new environment can feel isolated and lonely. They might also be given food they're not familiar with and have to adapt to new kinds of food. One way to make them feel 'at home' and cared for is to give them lots of foods they are familiar with and like. Visiting local shops that sells foods they like is a way of keeping a link with their background and building up a bond between child and new carer.

Many Caribbean shops, general markets, and supermarkets stock a rich variety of Caribbean and West African produce. Fruits like guava contain fewer calories than an apple, are rich in vitamin C, and potassium and mangoes are rich in vitamin A, iron and calcium. Vegetables like yams, dasheen, green banana and sweet potato provide a good range of vitamins, minerals, fibre and protein.

Ackee and saltfish

INGREDIENTS
For 4 people:-

- 1/2 lb saltfish (dried, salted codfish)
- 1 medium onion
- 1 sweet pepper
- 1/2 a hot chilli pepper (ideally Scotch bonnet)
- 1 sprig fresh thyme or 1 tsp dried thyme
- 1 tomato
- 3 tbsp of butter
- 1/2 tsp black pepper
- 12 fresh ackees or 1 (drained) can of tinned ackees

OPTIONAL INGREDIENTS
- 2 cloves of garlic
- 4 scallions (or spring onions)
- 6 bacon rashers

PREPARATION
Cover the saltfish in cold water. Leave to soak overnight (minimum 8 hours) changing the water several times (this removes most of the salt).
Bring a pan of cold water to the boil and gently simmer the fish for 20 minutes (until the fish is tender).
Chop the onion, sweet pepper, chilli pepper and tomato. Remove the fish from water and allow to cool.
Remove all bones and skin then flake the flesh of the fish.

COOKING INSTRUCTIONS
Melt the butter in a frying pan and stir fry the onion, black pepper, sweet pepper, chilli and thyme for about 3 minutes. Add the tomatoes and flaked fish and stir-fry for another 10 minutes. Add the ackee and cook until hot throughout. Stir gently to avoid breaking-up the ackee.

SERVING SUGGESTIONS
Serve with yam, green banana, fried dumplings and potato.

Jerk chicken

INGREDIENTS
For 4 people:-

- One 3½ lb chicken
  (3lb of chicken breasts may be used if preferred)
- 3 Medium onions
- 8 Cloves garlic
- 6 sliced scotch bonnet peppers (Jalapenos may
  be used if scotch bonnet peppers are unavailable)
- 2 tbsp. thyme
- 2 tsp. ground allspice
- 2 tsp. sugar
- 2 tsp. salt
- 2 tsp. ground black pepper
- 1 to 2 tsp ground cinnamon/nutmeg/ginger (to taste)
- 1/2 cup olive oil, 1/2 cup soy sauce, the juice of
  one lime
- 1 cup orange juice, 1 cup white vinegar

PREPARATION
Chop the onions, garlic and peppers. They do not need to be chopped too fine as they will be liquidised by the blender. Blend all of the ingredients (excluding the chicken) in a blender to make the jerk sauce. Cut the chicken into 4 pieces. Rub the sauce into the meat, saving some for basting and dipping later. Leave the chicken in the fridge to marinate overnight.

COOKING INSTRUCTIONS
Bake in the oven for 30 minutes. Turn the meat, then bake for a further 30 minutes. *Or* Grill the meat slowly until cooked, turning regularly. Baste with some of the remaining marinade while cooking.

SERVING SUGGESTIONS
Chop each chicken quarter into 5 or 6 smaller pieces using a heavy cleaver. Use a fork or a wooden spoon (or something similar) to hold the chicken in place while chopping NOT YOUR HAND (you will be chopping with enough pressure to cut through bone!!!) Jerk chicken can be served with rice and peas [see Glossary], or as a side dish with salad.

Cornmeal porridge

Porridge is a staple dish in many households. In the Caribbean, there are a variety of porridges - cornmeal, oats, sago (tapioca), plantain, flour and barley. Cornmeal, oats and sago are the most popular.

INGREDIENTS
For 2 people:-

- 1 cup of yellow cornmeal
- 4 cups of water
- 1 cup of milk
- 1/2 cup of sweetened condensed milk
- 1 tsp of vanilla
- 1/2 tsp of cinnamon
- 1/2 tsp of nutmeg
- Sugar to taste

COOKING INSTRUCTIONS
Place the cornmeal in a bowl and add 1 cup of the water. Mix together.
Mix milk and remaining 3 cups of water in a saucepan. Bring to the boil.
Once the water and milk have boiled turn down the heat and stir in the cornmeal mix.
Simmer for 10 minutes, stirring regularly.
Stir in the condensed milk, vanilla, cinnamon and nutmeg.
Simmer for a further 5 minutes.

SERVING SUGGESTIONS
Serve hot in a bowl.

Jollof rice

This Nigerian dish is the most popular rice recipe.

INGREDIENTS
For 4 people:-

- 1 medium onion (chopped)
- 1 red pepper
- 2 Scotch bonnet
- 1 garlic clove, crushed
- 1 tin plum tomato
- 1 small tin tomato purée
- 2 Maggi/Chicken Knorr cubes
- 2 tbsp cooking oil
- 500g (1.1 lbs) long grain (Easy cook rice)
- ½ tsp salt

COOKING INSTRUCTIONS

TO PREPARE THE SOUP
Chop the onion, red pepper, scotch bonnet and crushed garlic and place into a blender/liquidiser.
Add the tin of plum tomatoes and the tomato purée to the blender, along with the Maggi and chicken stock cubes. Then add 2 tbs of oil, and 2 cups of water. Blend all the ingredients together, until liquid and then pour into a pot.
Cook for 45minutes until the soup thickens. While the soup is cooking wash the rice thoroughly and leave aside.

TO PREPARE THE RICE
Cook the washed rice and add to the soup.
Cook the soup and rice together slowly for about half an hour on a low temperature, add salt to taste. If after half an hour the rice is still a little firm, add 2 tbs of cold water, allow to steam and soften for a further 30mins.

SERVING SUGGESTIONS
Serve with green salad.

Fried plantain

Fried plantain is a much loved delicacy in Africa and the Caribbean, served as an accompaniment to most meals. To ensure that the plantains are ripe, the skin should be almost black, or in some cases have a dull yellow colour with patches of black.

INGREDIENTS For 4 people:-
2 ripe plantains,
Shallow frying pan
Vegetable cooking oil

COOKING INSTRUCTIONS
Cut the ends of the plantains off, and along each of the ridges. Peel the skin away in sections.

Split the plantains in half width way, with a knife. Cut the plantain into bite-sized pieces (small circular pieces)
Fry the plantains in a frying pan for 15 minutes in a small amount of oil, until they begin to turn brown.

SERVING SUGGESTIONS
Serve as an accompaniment to a meal, with rice and salad.

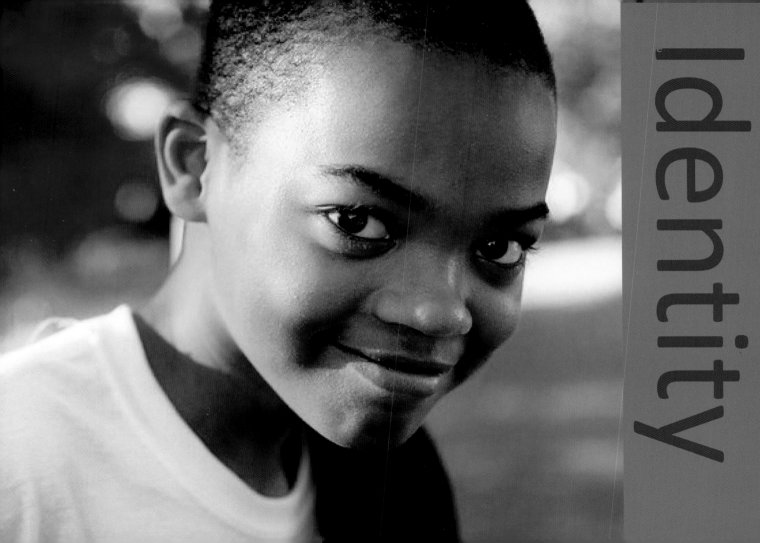

Identity

Self-esteem

It is important for black and mixed heritage children to develop good self-esteem and a positive attitude to their racial identity. However, one of the most overlooked challenges facing today's young black and mixed heritage children is self-esteem or lack of it. Self-esteem develops out of life's experiences, and is a product of children's early relationships, particularly with parents/foster carers/adopters and guardians. A child's identity should encompass a sense of positive self-esteem, confidence, and self-worth.

Families and carers are the important centre of values for black and mixed heritage children. Instilling positive self-esteem should not only start in the home, but within the parents themselves. Black and mixed heritage children need to know and feel that they are an important and valuable member of the family.

Foster carers, parents and other carers can bond with their child by understanding and help them to appreciate their unique hair and skin, which in turn will boost their self-esteem. Supporting black and mixed heritage children to learn about their culture, heritage and the contributions of their ancestors in helping to develop and shape society is an excellent way of building their self-esteem and confidence.

It is important to celebrate the child's background by showing positive images and books about their history and heritage.

The barber shop

Where do people go today just to talk with others in the community?

Men and young boys need traditions that can help bond them together. Visiting the barber with your parent is a great tradition to begin in your family. Many men have been going to the same barber all their life, and have then introduced their son to the same chair, and the same barber. Over a period of time good relationships develop.

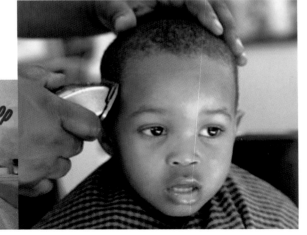

Today, one of the most important rites in a young black and mixed heritage boy's life is his first haircut at the barber shop. This is one of the places where a great deal of male socialisation takes place. In an earlier age, barber shops were places to meet others and learn about local news and what was going on in the neighbourhood. It was a real haven for black men, a place of security and comfort, and just a fascinating place to be.

Barber shops are a big influence in the black community. They are also places where youngsters learn from their elders, where they hear discussions about music, politics, sports and the meaning of life.

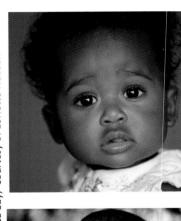

Culture, heritage and racial identity

From an early age children are aware of racial differences; However, development of a positive racial identity does not just happen, it must be cultivated. *Racial identity can be defined as an individual's perception and sense of belonging to a particular group.* According to this definition, racial and ethnic group differences will certainly impact on social development. Hence, social context, immediate surroundings and historical surroundings are underpinning factors in the development of the child's race awareness and cultural identify.

*Bath and North East Somerset Council

"A child with a strong racial identity will place high priority of his/her race as a component of self image."

Esther Ina-Egbe The Psychotherapist *Developing a Positive Racial Identity Spring 2010*

Studies show that black children in cross-cultural/ - transracial adoptive or foster placements place less significance on their race than do those adopted by black parents. ***"Having a mixed ethnic heritage has a different effect on a child's development, [Herring 1992]*** and it is important to actively help mixed children to acquire a positive self-concept. They need exposure to models of all the ethnicities they embrace, they need to understand what it means to be mixed heritage and they must have coping mechanisms to deal with racism. Foster carers and adoptive parents can engender this by having positive images, informative books, talking openly about the child's heritage, where they are from, and talking about their racial identity.

* The Psychotherapist Developing a Positive Racial Identity

In order to develop a truly positive identity for adopted children, families, schools and organisations should consider:

1. Recognising that black adopted children's knowledge and understanding of their cultural history are important.

2. Acknowledge the existence of prejudice, racism and discrimination

3. Explain why the child's minority group is mistreated.

4. Provide the child with a repertoire of responses to racial discrimination. Parents must work to minimise their children's feeling of helplessness. A child's identify can be more positive if he/she perceives him/herself and members of racial groups to be empowered with choices, resources, and the ability to acquire and protect their rights.

5. Provide the child with role models and positive contact with his/her minority group.

6. Prepare the child for discrimination; teach the child the difference between responsibility to, and responsibility for their minority groups.

7. Advocate on behalf of your child's positive racial identity; provide the child an environment that is conducive to the formation of a positive identity.

The Clark doll experiment 1939

The importance of racial identity for the black child in care cannot be underestimated. An experiment in 1939 highlighted the acute lack of racial identity awareness among black children in the United States, and studied children's attitude towards race. The experiment was conducted by Kenneth and Mamie in several US states. They asked black children to choose between a black doll and a white doll; the dolls were the same except for their skin colour. Most thought the white doll was nicer. The children were also asked to colour a picture of themselves, again most chose a shade of brown much lighter than themselves.

Clark doll experiment (1939)

In the experiment Clark showed black children between the ages of six and nine, two dolls, one white and one black, and then asked these questions in this order:

1 Show me the doll that you like best or that you'd like to play with.

2 Show me the doll that is the nice doll.

3 Show me the doll that looks bad.

4 "Give me the doll that looks like a white child."

5 "Give me the doll that looks like a coloured child."

6 "Give me the doll that looks like a Negro child."

7 "Give me the doll that looks like you."

The last question was the worst, since by that point most black children had chosen the black doll as the bad one. In 1950 44% said the white doll looked like them.

*Negro" and "coloured" were common terms for black people before the 1960s.

The doll experiment replicated by David Milner [1983] in the UK found that "Black British children showed a strong tendency for the dominant white majority and a tendency to devalue their own group". The film 'A Girl Like me'(Kiri Davis, 2005, USA) repeats the experiment, on a much smaller scale, but it is surprising to see how many black children still chose the white doll, in preference to the doll which most represented themselves.

Why do black dolls matter?

Decades after the famous doll experiment, it is still the case that many young black people lack self-esteem and a positive racial identity. Most of us think of dolls as children's play things, but dolls have a story to tell about race, culture, heritage and history. Black dolls can help to instil a sense of cultural identity and positive self-image.

It may seem like stating the obvious, but psychologists still emphasise the importance of black children seeing positive depiction of their own image, to boost their self-esteem and give them confidence. The issue of identity, racial identity, and self-esteem is tackled head on in the Samantha Knowles' film, **'Why do you have black dolls?** The film points out the importance of black children having dolls that reflect their racial identity, rather than the white, blonde haired and blue eyed dolls that are so common. Her film makes it clear that in terms of identity, black children should realise that there is nothing wrong with being black.

The future
*Rooti Dolls like many emerging black doll companies, is a company that produces dolls that are representative of black children, in order to give them positive images of themselves. *"The idea of* **Rooti dolls** *is to create that early interest in our children in their own culture, an appreciation of where they come from and to improve their self-esteem,"* Chris Chidi Ngoforo, founder of **Rooti Creations**.

Appendix

Books about hair
Glossary
Useful websites and online resources
Organisations
About the Authors
Notes

Books about hair

There are an increasing number of books for children about black and mixed heritage hair care. Some of the books talk about fun things to do with the children learning about their hair, how to feel good about it and how to look after it.

Other books illustrate how the hair is a critical component in developing a strong sense of racial identity. There are also a range of materials available to help carers/foster carers and adopters teach their children about how to care for their hair and skin properly. The books can be bought online and in most bookshops.

Glossary

Ackee and saltfish: Traditional Jamaican dish.

Adoption: A legal ruling that creates a parent-child relation between persons not related by blood; *[see fostering/foster child]*

African-Caribbean: People of African and Caribbean descent.

Afro: A natural hairstyle particular to African-Caribbean people.

Afro-comb: A wide toothed comb used to style and detangle Afro hair.

Antioxidants: A substance, such as vitamin E, vitamin C, or beta carotene, thought to protect body cells from the damaging effects of oxidation.

Aromatherapy: The use of plant extracts and essential oils in massage to promote physical and psychological well-being as part of a holistic treatment approach.

Atopic eczema: Caused by the immune system over-reacting to ordinary substances, e.g. dust mites.

Braid: A term used to describe plaiting or intertwining of hair. *[see plaiting]*

Caribbean: Means belonging or relating to the Caribbean Sea and its islands, or to its people and their culture.

Chlorine: A substance used for purifying water.

Cocoa butter: A moisturising cream used to nourish skin.

Coconut oil: The fatty oil obtained from the coconut and used in cosmetics.

Cornmeal porridge: Breakfast *[porridge]* made with cornmeal as a primary ingredient. It may also include milk, coconut milk, sugar and spices like nutmeg and vanilla.

Cornrow: A hairstyle plaited against the scalp.

Cortex: The outer part of an organ, or outer layer of tissue below the skin.

Cross-cultural placement: A child who is placed in a fostering placement which is different from their own cultural background.

Culture: The customs, achievements, attitudes and behavioural characteristic of a particular group.

Cultural heritage: The things, places and practices that define who we are as individuals, as communities, as nations or civilisations, which we want to keep, share and pass on.

Cultural identity: The identity of a group or culture.

Cuticle: The strip of hardened skin at the base of a fingernail or toenail.

Dasheen: Edible starchy tuberous root of taro plants. *[see taro plant]*

Dermatitis: A general term used to describe inflammation of the skin. Most types of dermatitis are characterized by an itchy pink or red rash.

Detangle: To untangle hair.

Essential oils: Oils extracted from plants and flowers that have specific characteristics, which determine their use – they can be stimulating or relaxing or even anti-bacterial and healing. Usually inhaled or used in treatment such as massages, where they are absorbed into the skin.

Eczema: A non-contagious inflammation of the skin, characterised chiefly by redness, itching.

Fostering/foster child: Caring for a child without parental support and protection, placed with a person or family to be cared for, usually by local welfare services or by court order. *[See adoption]*

Green banana: The unripe banana used as a vegetable in soup or made as porridge. In this state it is a rich source of iron.

Guardians: A person who has been appointed by a judge to take care of a minor child (called a "ward") and/or manage that person's affairs.

Haematologist: A doctor with a specialty in treating blood disorders.

Hair Moisturiser: Natural substances/products that are used to feed and nurture hair.

Heritage: Something an individual is born to, that which passes from one generation to the next in a social group e.g. a way of life or traditional culture.

Holistic: To take account of a persons, physical, mental and social conditions when treating an illness.

Hyper pigmentation: A disfiguring and discolouring of the skin.

Inflammation: A swelling, redness, heat and pain produced in an area of the body as a reaction to injury or infection.

Jojoba oil: A large American plant with sharp leaves whose seeds contain oil which is used in beauty products.

Jollof rice: A West African stew made with rice, chilli peppers, and meat or fish.

Keratin: A structural protein molecule, which is found in hair, nails and in the skin.

Kinky: Term used to refer to the typical texture of Black hair that has not been altered by hot combs, flat irons, or chemicals (by perming, relaxing, or straightening).

Leave-in conditioner: Hair moisturizer that keeps hair healthy, giving it body and shine.

Lint: A term used to describe, the particles that are left when hair is not groomed or combed.

Locs: A hairstyle traditionally worn by Rastafarians, created by plaiting and twisting locs of hair.

Massage: A treatment that involves rubbing the muscles, either for medical or therapeutic purposes or simply as an aid to relaxation.

Medulla: The innermost area of organs or tissue; e.g. Hair.

Melanin: A dark brown to black skin pigmentation found in African/Caribbean and mixed heritage people.

Mixed heritage: A term used to describe children who have parents from different races.

Moisturiser: A cream/oil that is put on the skin or scalp to stop it from becoming dry.

Natural hair: A term used to describe black hair that has not been treated with chemicals, perming, relaxing or straightening.

Nok: A group of people living in Nigeria between 500BC and AD 300, who were known for their highly developed style of Art.

Nutrition: The process of absorbing nutrients from food, and processing them to keep our body healthy.

Omega-3 oils: Essential to human health, omega-3 oils (fatty acids) are a form of polyunsaturated fats found in fish, seeds, nuts and oils.

Organic: Skincare products or products made from natural products that are free from preservatives or additives, and contain no harmful bacteria.

Plaiting: A hair style made from twisting three or more strands of hair, over and under each other to make one single piece.

Plantain fritters: A sweet food popular in the Caribbean

Protein: A complex natural substance essential to the structure and function of all living cells.

Protective style: Relating to the plaiting of hair, keeping the hair up and the ends away, avoiding breaking.

Race: A group of people connected by common descent/features.

Rastafarian: A member of a religious sect, originating in Jamaica.

Residential units: A residential unit or home where young people *[CIC] live, who are being looked after by the Local Authority. *Children in Care

Rice and peas: A dish made from rice and peas or beans. Red kidney beans or gungo peas are commonly used. The dish is prepared with coconut milk and seasoning.

Self-esteem: A belief in yourself, and having confidence in your own ability and value.

Shea butter: A moisturising cream made from the fat of the nut, borne from the West African tree, *'Vitellaria Paradoxa.'*

Sheen: A lustre, or brightness, gained when black hair is oiled and conditioned.

Sickle cell: The formation of red blood cells into an abnormal crescent *[sickle]* shape.

Sickle cell anaemia: A medical condition, found especially in black people, in which the red blood cells are curved **[sickle]** in shape.

Sun screen/block: A substance put on your skin to prevent it from being burnt by the sun.

Sweet potato: Large thick sweet and nutritious tuberous root that is cooked and eaten as a vegetable, or used to make puddings or cakes.

Taro plant: A stemless plant grown in the Pacific Islands. **[see dasheen]**

Wide-tooth comb: A comb used to style and detangle Afro hair. **[see Afro comb]**

Yam: A staple food in many tropical countries, particularly in Africa, the Caribbean and the South Pacific. Yams have brown tough skins and the flesh can vary in colour – anything from white to yellow to purple.

Online resources

Culture heritage and identity

www.blackhistorystudies.com
www.naturalnovember.co.uk
www.onehandcantclap.co.uk
Kaipersonaldesigns@yahoo.co.uk
www.colorblindcards.com
Akhudesigns@gmail.com
http://arhinarmah.co.uk
info@afrodeity.co.uk
www.rootidolls.com
http://www.blackbeautydolls.com
http://4kidslikeme.com
mixedracefamilies.blogspot.co.uk
http://store.afrodeity.co.uk
rwchessacademy@hotmail.com
www.afridiziak.com

info@afridiziak.com
www.colouryoursuccess.com

Education/books/writing

www.greenshackproductions.com
www.eduzone.co.uk
www.isisempire.com
www.amazon.com
www.amazon.com/Black-Childrens-Hair-Books
www.amazon.com/African-American-Children-Books
http://tiptopcat.hubpages.com/hub/Black-Childrens-Books-About-Hair
www.brownbabyreads.com/haircarepage.html
www.icecreamtoysandbooks.com
www.binoandfino.com

www.comeunity.com/adoption/books/
0blackhaircare.html
http://about.me/juanrose
workerbee2queenbee.com
www.newbeaconbooks.co.uk
www.brownskinbooks.co.uk
www.leeandlow.com

Health and well-being
www.amennoir.com
amennoir@yahoo.co.uk
www.aclt.org
www.skinhelp.co.uk
www.sicklecellsociety.org
www.ayannaaromas.co.uk
ayannaaromas@hotmail.com

Natural hair care
www.beuniquehaircare.co.uk
www.bespokehairstyles.com
www.maatmovements.com
www.root2tip.com
www.thecalabashhub.com
www./iloveafro.co.uk
www.afrotherapy.ccom
www.iloveafro.co.uk
www.naturallyrandom.com
www.thenaturallounge.com
www.naturalblackhaircare.com
www.going-natural.com
www.britishcurlies.co.uk
www.dias-allnatural.co.uk
www.holisticlocs.com

www.naturesparlour.co.uk
www.afrocenchix.com
www.gtbnatural.co.uk
www.hairnaturel.co.uk
www.theafrohairandskincompany.com
www.howtodread.com
www.abeni.co.uk
www.curlharmony.co.uk
www.growafrohairlong.com
www.happygirlhair.com
www.hairwegrownatural.com
www.mycurls.co.uk
www.prettycurls.com
www.roots2ends.co.uk
www.morris-roots.com
www.lizearle.com/naturalhair
www.azizanaturalbeauty.com

www.naturallysexy.co.uk
www.afrotherapy.com
www.blackhairinformation.com
www.going-natural.com

Natural skin care

www.alberthasgarden.co.uk
www.sheadecadence.co.uk
www.OilsandBotany.com
www.sheadelight.co.uk
www.akomaskincare.co.uk
www.yessessentials.com
www.thegoodyboxuk.co.uk
www.sheabuttercottage.co.uk
ceo@premaeskincare.com
www.premaeskincare.com
info@puregoodnesshairandskin.com

www.imanmade.com
www.ooohskincare.com
www.mama-sia.com
www.brownskin.net
www.naturalelle.co.uk

**UK wide adoption &
fostering organisations**
www.BAAF.org.uk
www.chrysaliscarefostering.org
www.newfamilysocial.org.uk
www.rainbowfostering.co.uk
www.barnados.org.uk
www.kidsco.org.uk
www.NSPCC.org.uk
www.nfa.co.uk
www.adoptionsearchreunion.org
www.actionforchildren.org.uk

www.adoption uk.org
www.bemyparent.org.uk
www.thefostercareagency.org.uk

Young people/self-esteem
winston.goode@londonyouth.org.uk
www.beleveuk.org
http://mixedracefamilies.blogspot.co.uk
http://janetlifecoach.blogspot.co.uk
http://www.multiculturalfamilia.com
www.moniqueneeley.com
http://chessforchildren.influencer.biz
Nadine.woodley@gmail.com
Hiype.productions@gmail.com
samanthacalliste@gmail.com
www.100bmol.org.uk
www.hackneychild.co.uk

Organisations:

Action for Children UK
Head office: Action for Children,
3 The Boulevard, Ascot Road,
Watford WD18 8AG
Phone: 01923 361500
www.actionforchildren.org.uk

ACLT
Southbridge House,
Southbridge Place
Croydon,
Surrey CR0 4HA
Phone: 0208 240 4480
Fax: 0208 240 4481
Email: info@aclt.org
www.aclt.org

Adoption Counselling London
Phone: 0208 994 3580
Email: info@adoptioncounselling
london.com
www.adoptioncounsellinglondon.com

BAAF British Adoption and Fostering
Saffron House, 6-10 Kirby Street
London, EC1N 8TS
Phone: 0207 421 2600
Fax: 0207 421 2601
Email: mail@baaf.org.uk
www.baaf.org.uk

Barnardo's Head Office
Scotch House, Tanners Lane,
Barkingside, Ilford, Essex, IG6 1QG
Phone: 0208 550 8822
Fax: 0208 551 6870
Email: Supportercare@barnardos.org.uk
www.barnardos.org.uk

Fostering Network (The)
87 Blackfriars Road
London, SE1 8HA
Phone: 0207 620 6400
Fax: 0207 620 6401
Email: info@fostering.net
www.fostering.net

Kids Company
London Centre: Arches II
1 Kenbury Street
London SE5 9BS
Phone: 44 (0) 207 274 8378
Email: info@kidsco.org.uk
www.kidsco.org.uk

Headquarters (NSPCC)
**National Society for the Prevention
of Cruelty to Children,**
Weston House,
42 Curtain Road,
London EC2A 3NH
Switchboard: 0207 825 2500
Fax: 0207 825 2525
Email: help@nspcc.org.uk
www.nspcc.org.uk

**National Fostering Agency
Uxbridge Head Office:**
71 Cowley Road,
Uxbridge, UB8 2AE
Phone: 01895 200300
Email: info@nfa.co.uk
www.nfa.co.uk

**Ofsted
London Office,** Aviation House,
125 Kingsway,
London WC2B 6SE
General Helpline: 0300 123 1231
Email: enquiries@ofsted.gov.uk
www.ofsted.gov.uk

About the authors

Flora Awolaja

An ardent educationalist, achievement for all is central to the work that Flora does. A successful career as a graphic designer has allowed Flora to combine her passion for art and design with teaching. As a lecturer, Flora works to raise achievement in all learners, by encouraging them, raising their self-esteem, and aspiring confidence in them. Flora's fun loving and exuberant personality exudes a quiet confidence and steely determination to succeed in all things.

Denise Lewis

A qualified, successful social work practitioner, with over 20 years' experience in the public social care sector, Denise has always been innovative and dynamic within her practice. She has worked within inner and outer London boroughs and is a good organiser of groups for service users who have mental health challenges. Throughout her career Denise has been a strong advocate of equal opportunities and diversity Denise's area of expertise includes fostering, child protection and safe-guarding. Denise is a mother of four teenage children.

Notes